Phil Collins Anthology.

Exclusive Distributors

Music Sales Limited
8/9 Frith Street, London W1V 5TZ England

Music Sales Pty. Limited
120 Rothschild Avenue, Rosebery, NSW 2018 Australia

This book © Copyright 1985 by Music Publications
Order No. AM 61243
ISBN 0-7119-0775-7

Book design by Pearce Marchbank Studio

Printed in the United Kingdom by
Scotprint Limited, Musselburgh, Edinburgh

Music Sales complete catalogue lists thousands
of titles and is free from your local music bookshop
or direct from Music Sales Limited.
Please send a cheque/postal order for £1.50 for postage to
Music Sales Limited, Newmarket Road, Bury St. Edmunds, Suffolk IP33 3YB

In The Air Tonight..

Words and Music by Phil Collins.

This Must Be Love.

Words and Music by Phil Collins.

It must be love _____ I'm feel-ing, this must be love ___

___ oh, this must be love _____ I'm feel-ing,

this must be love. ___

Well I wait in ev-
Hap-pi-ness is some-thing
Words can on-ly say ___

Behind The Lines.

Words and Music by Phil Collins, Tony Banks and Mike Rutherford.
© Copyright 1980 Crossound Ltd./Effectsound Ltd./Spreadsound Ltd.
Administered by Hit & Run Music (Publishing) Ltd. London W.1.
All Rights Reserved. International Copyright Secured.

The Roof is Leaking

Words and Music by Phil Collins

The roof is leak-ing and the wind is howl-ing, kids are cry-ing 'cause the
Ma and Pa lived here and theirs be - fore them, they tried their hardest to

sheets are so cold. I woke this morn-ing, found my hands were fro - zen
make it a home. seems so long now since they passed ov - er

I've tried to fix the fire but you know the damn thing's too cold
hope my child-ren 'll try to make it their own.

Droned.

Words and Music by Phil Collins
© Copyright 1981 Effectsound Ltd. / Hit & Run Music (Publishing) Ltd. London W.1.
All Rights Reserved. International Copyright Secured.

I Missed Again.

So you

fin - al - ly came right out and said it,___ girl   what took you
I think a - bout it from time to___ time   when I'm lone -

You Know What I Mean.

Words and Music by Phil Collins.

Just as I thought I'd made it

you walk back in-to my life, Just like you nev-er left.

I'm Not Moving.

Words and Music by Phil Collins.

Hand In Hand.

Words and Music by Phil Collins.

Thunder And Lightning

Words and Music by Phil Collins

I nev - er real - ly___ thought I'd get tired of play - ing___ games___
I nev - er ev - er___ did___ be - lieve in guid - ing___ lights___
I nev - er ev - er___ did___ be - lieve in sec - ond___ chance___

they said ___ thun - der and they said ___ light - ning ___

it would nev - er strike twice Oh - ho ___ but

if that's ___ true, then why can't you tell ___ me ___

how come this feels so nice ___ so nice, when

Repeat to Fade

If Leaving Me Is Easy

Words and Music by Phil Collins

Tomorrow Never Knows

Words and Music by John Lennon and Paul McCartney
© Copyright 1966 Northern Songs Ltd., London W.1.
All Rights Reserved. International Copyright Secured.

Turn off your mind,— re-lax and float down-stream—
love is all— and love is ev-'ry one—

It is not dy-ing,— it is not dy - ing.—
It is know-ing,— oh it is know - ing.—

Lay down all thoughts,— sur-ren-der to— the void—
And ig-nor-ance— and hate may mourn— the dead.

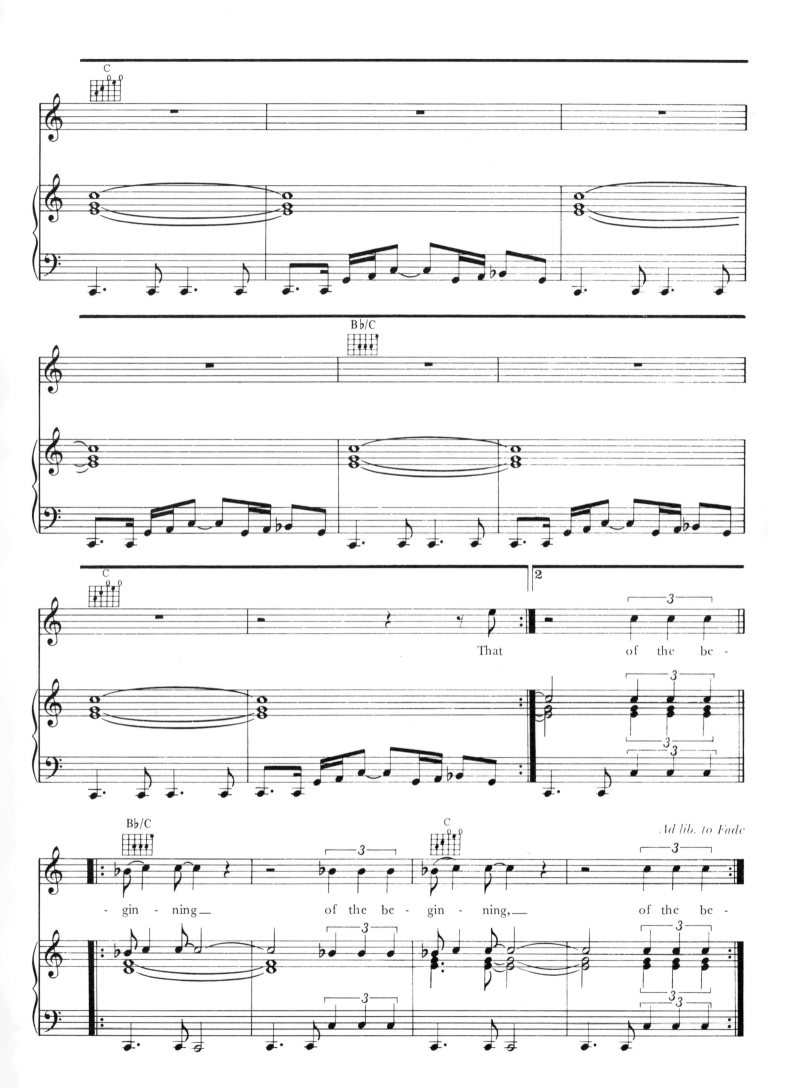

Don't Let Him Steal Your Heart Away

Words and Music by Phil Collins

Don't let him steal— your heart— a-way—

No, don't

let him steal—your heart——— a-way.—

2 & 3

And don't pack my suit-case,

I'll be back

And don't take my pic-tures off—— a {the / your} wall—

Thru' These Walls

Words and Music by Phil Collins

1 & %. I can hear thru' these walls—— I can hear it when they're
2. I can see thru' my win—— dows I can see the

fool-in' a-round.—— I can hear thru' these walls——
girls and the boys.—— I can see thru' my win——

—— and I hear ev-'ry sign,—— ev-'ry sound.——
——dows and can im-a—— gine the noise.——

Why Can't It Wait Till Morning?

Words and Music by Phil Collins.

Why can't— it wait 'til morn-ing?

We— can talk a-bout — it then.— 'Cos I've—had a drink too ma-ny

I Don't Care Anymore

Words and Music by Phil Collins

Well you can tell ev-'ry-one I'm a down— dis-grace.—
talk-ing to the peo-ple that you call your friends— and it
-mem-ber all the times I tried— so hard— and you

Drag my— name all— o-ver the place.— I don't
seems to— me there's a means to an end.—They don't } care an-y-more.
laughed in my face 'cos you held all the cards.— I don't

Like China

Words and Music by Phil Collins

My mom and dad-dy both say I must be cra-zy to be this in - fat — u - at - ed
Your mum and dad don't like — me And they tell me eve-ry time — I call a - round — to see you

But I — know you — know — we got some - thing spe-cial nev-er felt be-fore. —
I don't — know why — 'cos I always straighten my tie and comb my hair. —

Do You Know, Do You Care?

Words and Music by Phil Collins.

It Don't Matter To Me.

Well
That) it don't matter to me——— what you say,——— what you say

And
Well) it don't matter to me——— what you're do———ing—al-right,— al——right.

The West Side.

Words by Phil Collins

You Can't Hurry Love.

Words and Music by Eddie Holland, Lamont Dozier and Brian Holland.
© Copyright 1965 Jobete Music Co. Inc. USA. Jobete Music (UK) Ltd, London W.1.
All Rights Reserved. International Copyright Secured.

I Cannot Believe It's True.

Words and Music by Phil Collins

Sussudio.

Words and music by Phil Collins
© Copyright 1984 Phil Collins Ltd. / Hit & Run Music (Publishing) Ltd. London W.1.
All Rights Reserved. International Copyright Secured.

There's a girl that's been on my
Now I know that I'm too

mind _____ all the time _____ sus - sus-sud-
young _____ my life has just be - gun _____ sus - sus-sud-

Only You Know And I Know.

Words and Music by Phil Collins and Daryl Stuermer

Long Long Way To Go.

Words and Music by Phil Collins.
© Copyright 1984 Phil Collins Ltd / Hit & Run Music (Publishing) Ltd. London W.1.
All Rights Reserved. International Copyright Secured.

While I sit here try-ing to think_
While I sit here try-ing to move_
While we sit and we talk and talk_

___ of things to say___
___ you an-y-way I can___
___ and we talk some more._

some-one lies bleed-ing in a field some-
some-one's son lies dead in a
Some-one's loved one's heart stops

where.
gut-ter some-where.
beat-ing in a street some-where.

So you can see we still got a
And it would seem we've still got a
So it would seem we've still got a

long long way to go.
long long way to go.
long long way to go. (I know)

I've seen all I wan-na see to-day.
I can't take it an-y more.
I've heard all I wan-na hear to-day.

Turn it off if you want to switch it off it will go a - way.

Page 104

I Don't Wanna Know.

Words and Music by Phil Collins and Daryl Stuermer
© Copyright 1984. Phil Collins Ltd. / Hit & Run Music (Publishing) Ltd. London W.1.
All Rights Reserved. International Copyright Secured.

One More Night.

Words and Music by Phil Collins
© Copyright 1984 Phil Collins Ltd/Hit & Run Music (Publishing)Ltd. London W.1.
All Rights Reserved. International Copyright Secured.

one more night___ 'cause I can't_ wait for ev - er.

ooh ooh ooh ___

ooh ooh ooh ___ ooh ooh ooh ___

ooh ooh ooh ___

Don't Lose My Number

Words and music by Phil Collins

oh Bil - ly, you __ bet - ter, you __

__ bet - ter, you __ bet-ter run __ for your life. __

Bil - ly, Bil - ly don't you lose my num - ber,

Who Said I Would?

Words and Music by Phil Collins

well there ain't no oth - er way._____ But she's got a a
And then she sets me free._____ 'Cause she's got a a
know it's her bo - dy not her mind._____ And she's got a a

heart, must be made of stone _____ 'cause when I tell her that she'll miss me when I'm gone,

_____ she says who said I would.

She

Tell__ me, who said I would,____

Inside Out.

Words and Music by Phil Collins

In - side   out,___   oh you got me   in - side   out___

in - side   out,___   oh   oh   in - side   out.___

(After rpt.)
To Coda ⊕

Take Me Home.

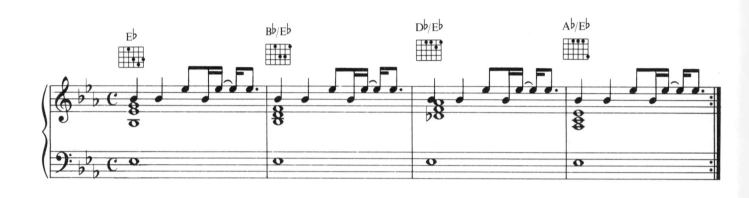

Take that look of_ wor-ry,   I'm an or-di-na-ry man_
Seems so long I've_ been wait-ing   still don't know_ what for_
Take that look of_ wor-ry   mine's an or-di-na-ry life_

they_don't tell_ me no - thing   so I
there's no point_ es - cap - ing   I don't
work-ing when_ it's_ day - light   and

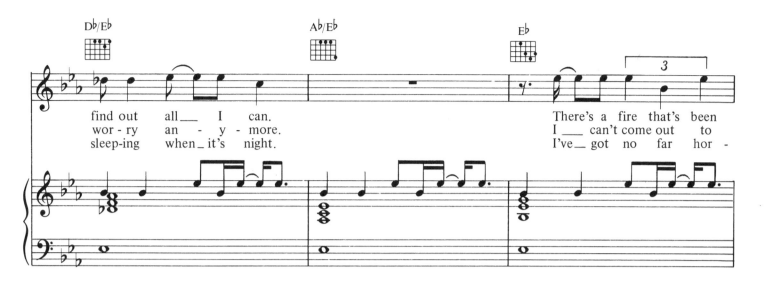

find out all __ I can.
wor - ry an - y - more.
sleep-ing when __ it's night.

There's a fire that's been
I __ can't come out to
I've __ got no far hor -

burn - ing
find you
iz - ons

right out - side __ my _____ door. _____
I don't like to go __ out - side _____
I don't wish up - on __ a _____ star.

I __ can't see but I feel it
They can turn off my feel-ings
They don't think that I lis - ten

and it helps to keep __ me warm.
like they're turn - ing off __ the light.
oh but I know who __ they are. __

Doesn't Anybody Stay Together Anymore?

Words and Music by Phil Collins and Daryl Stuermer
© Copyright 1984 Phil Collins Ltd./ Hit & Run Music (Publishing) Ltd. London W.1.
All Rights Reserved. International Copyright Secured.

well, there's just an emp-ty space. ____ And there's noth - ing

left__ here__ to re-mind __ me, __ just the mem - 'ry of__ your face. ____ Well, take a look at me now. __

1. well, there's just an   emp-ty space.____   And you com - in' back__
2. 'cause there's just an   emp-ty space.____   But to wait__
3. 'cause I'll still be   stand-ing here.____   And you com - in' back__

__ to me __ is a - gainst __ the odds,____ and that's what __ __ I've got __ to face.__
__ for you __ is all____ I   can do,____ and that's what
__ to me __ is a - gainst____ all odds, _____ it's the chance

I __ I've got__ to face. Take a good look at me now.__

__I've got__ to take. _____

Take a look at me now._____

Verse 2:
How can you just walk away from me,
When all I can do is watch you leave?
'Cause we shared the laughter and the pain,
And even shared the tears.
You're the only one who really knew me at all.
(To Chorus:)

Verse 3:
I wish I could just make you turn around,
Turn around and see me **cry.**
There's so much I need to say to you,
So many reasons why.
You're the only one who really knew me at all.
(To Chorus:)

Easy Lover.

Checklist of important piano books.
The books below are available from your local music shop
who will order them for you if not in stock.
If there is no music shop near you, you may order direct from
Music Sales Limited (Dept. M), 8/9 Frith Street, London W1V 5TZ.
Please always include £1 to cover post/packing costs.

A Start At The Piano
AM 40650

**Alison Bell's Graded
For Piano Pieces
Book 1: Very Easy**
AM 30297

**Book 5: Upper
Intermediate**
AM 30339

**Anthology Of Piano
Music Volume 1:
Baroque**
AM 10968

Volume 3: Romantic
AM 10984

**Barrelhouse And Boogie
Piano**
OK 64659

**Big Note Piano
Book 1**
AM 28226

**Bud Powell: Jazz
Masters Series**
AM 23219

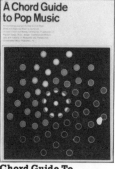

**Chord Guide To
Pop Music**
AM 10596

**The Classic Piano
Repertoire Bach**
EW 50023

Chopin
EW 50015

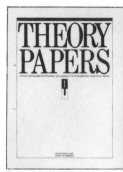

**Promenade Theory
Papers Book 1**
PB 40583

**Classics To Moderns
Book 1**
YK 20014

**Classics To Moderns
Sonatas & Sonatinas**
YK 20204

Themes & Variations
YK 20196

**More Classics To
Moderns Book 1**
YK 20121

**Dave Brubeck: Jazz
Masters Series**
AM 21189

**Easy Classical Piano
Duets**
AM 31949

**The Complete Piano
Player By Kenneth
Baker Book 1**
AM 34828

Book 2
AM 34836

Book 3
AM 34844

Book 4
AM 34851

Book 5
AM 34869

Style Book
AM 35338

Improvising Rock Piano
AM 22039

Easy Piano Solos
Simple Arrangements
of Pop Classics
AM 28648

**For Your Eyes Only & 18
Movie Themes**
AM 36609

**Genius Of George
Shearing**
AM 25990

Genius Of Art Tatum
BG 10085

Genius Of Fats Waller
AM 24423

Genius of Andre Previn
AM 25982

**Genius Of Jazz Giants
Volume 1**
AM 36708

Jazz Hanon
AM 27418

Blues Hanon
AM 27889

Boogie Woogie Hanon
AM 27400

**Home Piano Library
Classics**
AM 34141

Rock 'n' Roll
AM 36922

Showmusic
AM 36724

Hooked On Classics
AM 32210

How To Play Blues Piano
AM 35197

**How To Play Boogie-
Woogie**
AM 33317

Improvising Rock Piano
AM 22039

Ballet Music
AM 32939

Beatles
NO 17907

Rock and Roll
AM 19556

Elvis
AM 20868

Familiar Songs
AM 36419

Paul Simon
PS 10214

Christmas Songs
AM 22641

Walt Disney
WD 10260

Jazz Riffs For Piano
AM 21502

**The Joy Of
Bach**
YK 21004

Boogie and Blues
YK 21020

Christmas
YK 21194

Folk Songs
YK 21061

Mozart
YK 21244

Piano Entertainment
YK 21178

Romantic Piano: Book 1
YJK 21145

First Year Piano
YK 21053

Piano Duets
YK 21111

Pianist's Picture Chords
AM 21429

The Piano Chord Finder
AM 24860

More Piano Pieces For Children
YK 20220

The Music Of Michel Legrand
AM 25727

Piano Adventures Pop Blends
AM 32079

I Love Pop
AM 32087

Popular Piano Solos Book 1
AM 24100

Book 7: Blues
AM 33879

Book 8: Jazz
AM 33861

Easy Classical Piano Duets
AM 31949

Easy Folk Piano Duets
AM 31956

Ragtime: 100 Authentic Rags
AM 25081

Rock Keyboard Styles
(with cassette)
DG 20017

The Best Of McCartney Easy Piano
MY 70101

Songs Of World War II
AM 14226

Teach Yourself Rock Piano
AM 25172

Teaching Piano (Combined) By Denes Agay.
YK 20279

Thelonious Monk: Jazz Masters Series
AM 19423

They All Played Ragtime
OK 61572

Timeless Standards
AM 36641

Timeless Country Standards
AM 36658

Timeless Jazz Standards
AM 36666

Tomorrow: 18 Broadway Blockbusters
AM 36617

With My Love
AM 25925

10/91 (12534)